1. The first USAF combat wing to convert from A-7Ds to A-10s began to do so in March 1977. These are four aircraft for the 354th TFW based at Myrtle Beach, South Carolina. (Fairchild Republic)

WARBIRDS ILLUSTRATED NO. 40

A10 THUNDERBOLT II

DANA BELL

ARMS AND ARMOUR PRESS

Introduction

Published in 1986 by Arms & Armour Press Ltd.,
2–6 Hampstead High Street, London NW3 1QQ.

Distributed in the United States by Sterling
Publishing Co. Inc., 2 Park Avenue, New York,
N.Y. 10016.

British Library Cataloguing in Publication Data:
Bell, Dana
A10 Thunderbolt II. – (Warbirds Illustrated)
1. A-10 (Jet attack plane)
I. Title   II. Series
623.74′64   UG1242.A28

ISBN 0-85368-772-2

Editing, design and artwork by Roger Chesneau.
Typesetting by Typesetters (Birmingham) Ltd.
Printed and bound in Italy by GEA/GEP in
association with Keats European Ltd., London.

It seems generous to call the Fairchild Republic A-10 a fighter, at least by modern standards: whilst most modern fighters are capable of performing an air-to-air mission, the A-10 is limited to the glamourless close air support role. The A-10 does not carry a radar, it cannot rely on high speed for pursuit or escape, and it cannot climb high into the stratosphere beyond the range of ground-based weapons. The A-10 seems to be better classed with the medium bombers of the Second World War such as the North American B-25 Mitchell!

In fact, specifications for the A-10 closely parallel those of the Mitchell: wing span, length and height are almost identical. The A-10's empty weight is only 700lb greater, but with a maximum load the A-10 weighs almost six tons more than the B-25H's eighteen tons. At those weights, the A-10 carries 16,000lb of ordnance compared with the B-25H's 3,200lb. (Much of the B-25's maximum weight was accounted for by five additional crew members and defensive armaments, though there may well be times that an A-10 driver would wish for a tail gunner.) Both aircraft are known for large cannon. The B-25H's 75mm gun was slow-firing and inaccurate and soon discarded in combat use, but the 30mm cannon of the A-10 is a powerful and accurate weapon. With a top speed in the same class as the Mustang or Spitfire, it would seem that the A-10 would have been quite a contender forty years ago!

Since the Second World War, many in the US Air Force have been calling for an aircraft with just these capabilities, and now there is no other aircraft able accurately to deliver as much ordnance to the front lines as can the A-10. Expecting to take hits, it is designed to survive and fly, to be easily repaired, and to fight again. As for defending itself, an F-14 pilot once told me about trying to make gun passes on an A-10: as he moved in, the A-10 pilot turned and reversed. The Navy pilot still seemed amazed as he recounted the story: 'As I flashed by, I could see him turn with me. That big old gun was pointed right at my helmet all the way!'

The majority of the photographs in this book have come from the USAF (through the kind offices of Major Bill Austin and Lt June Green) and Fairchild Republic (with my old friend Theron Rinehart, now retired). Don Linn, Greg Marshall, Dave Menard, Rob Stern and Wally van Winkle came to my assistance as they always do. As a writer and a reader, I would like to thank Lionel Leventhal for keeping the *Warbirds* series interesting and enjoyable. Colleen and Geoffrey got a chance to help sort pictures (they like the 'aircraft with the spots'), and Susan's support has kept me going when I thought I'd never again want to see another black and white print, colour slide or word processor. My thanks to them all!

Dana Bell

◄2
2. An A-10 on deployment to Europe is refuelled as crewmen work in the cockpit, 1978. (Fairchild Republic)

3. Technicians at NASA's Ames Research Center mount a model of the A-10 for wind tunnel tests in 1972. Prototype flight tests would later improve airflow at the wing roots, but the balance of the design was basically unchanged prior to production. (USAF)

4. The second of the two YA-10 prototypes. External stores mounted here are two 2,000lb bombs (outboard of the wheel sponsons) and twenty-two 500-pounders. The 20mm Vulcan cannon originally installed on the prototypes is visible in the nose. (Fairchild Republic)

5. Not all tests involved flying: ground-handling tests included high speed taxis through puddles to monitor landing gear efficiency and water ingestion by engines. Note the aft-facing camera mounted above the national insignia. (USAF)

6. Northrop's YA-9 was in direct competition with the A-10 for production as the USAF's primary close air support aircraft. The January 1972 production decision relegated the A-9 to be remembered as an 'also ran' in books about the A-10. (USAF)

◄ 3

4 ▲

5 ▲　　6 ▼

▲7

7. A dummy refuelling receptacle was mounted on the first prototype to test stability in formation with tankers. August 1974. (USAF)

8. An Edwards test pilot maintains formation, snuggled up behind a Boeing KC-135, in 1972. A 30mm GAU-8 Avenger cannon has replaced the 20mm Vulcan in this prototype's nose, and repainting has removed the letters 'US' from the forward fuselage. (Fairchild Republic)

9. Along with the GAU-8, the AGM-65 Maverick missile is considered a principal weapon for the A-10. In this photograph six cameras surround the missiles mounted on the first prototype for a September 1974 stores evaluation flight. The first A-10 Maverick launches occurred later in the month. (USAF)

10. Firing tests suggested a revised mounting for the GAU-8, depressing the gun two degrees and extending its length several inches by December 1974. (USAF)

▼8

▲11   ▼12
13▶

11. Near the end of its flight test career, in March 1975, the first prototype carried Mk 20 cluster bombs for a stores compatibility flight. The aircraft's last flight was in June 1975. (USAF)
12. With slow landing speeds, the A-10 has no use for parachutes, although here the repainted second prototype deploys a parachute at

Edwards in 1974. The system was later used for spin tests. (USAF)
13. This LTV A-7D was evaluated against the second prototype in Kansas in 1974 in tests mandated by Congress. Both aircraft were painted overall 'gunship gray' for the competition. (USAF)

▲14   ▼15

16▲

14. This 1975 photo, one of a well-known series by Air Force photographer Ken Hackman, shows the two A-10 prototypes and four of the six pre-production airframes on the Edwards flight-line. The Air Force evaluated various camouflages on the A-10, which by this time had been dubbed 'Warthog' by its crews. (Fairchild Republic)
15. The first pre-production aircraft, with three ferry tanks, on a stores certification flight. With its instrument boom removed and an updated paint scheme applied, this aircraft would appear almost identical to the last A-10A, which was produced 712 airframes later. (Fairchild Republic)
16. The second pre-production airframe was delivered with an overall white colour scheme; the primer undercoat was black. (Fairchild Republic)
17. After several months of test flights, enough white had worn away to leave an extremely mottled appearance. The weapons mounted in this photograph are 500lb laser-guided bombs. (USAF)

17▼

▲18   ▼19

18. Roll out of aircraft No. 3. Most A-10s wore only a primer coat for acceptance flights before a trip to the paint shop. (Fairchild Republic)
19. Aircraft No. 4 moves into a refuelling position behind a Boeing KC-135 tanker over Edwards AFB. (USAF)
20. Tanks refilled, No. 4 banks away to display a load of eighteen 500lb bombs. The fuselage racks mount bombs on MERs (Multiple Ejector Racks) each carrying six weapons, but in the event MERs were not certified for use on operational A-10s. (USAF)

▲21

21. Beginning in March 1976, production aircraft were assigned to the 355th TFW at Davis-Monthan AFB, Arizona, for operational evaluation and aircrew training. Note here the 355th's 'DM' tail code on the lead aircraft. (USAF)

22. The final pre-production aircraft pulls in its landing gear for a stores test in 1976. (USAF)

23. A technician applies the shield of the Tactical Air Command (TAC) to the tail of a pre-production aircraft. TAC accepted control of the A-10 project in mid-1976. (Fairchild Republic)

▼22

23▶

▲24

24. The Mk 20 Rockeye is one of the USAF's standard cluster weapons. Here, four Rockeyes wait to be loaded on to the fifth pre-production aircraft at Edwards in 1976. (USAF)
25. An A-10 dives on its target. Underwing are four Rockeyes and

▼25

two Maverick training missiles. (USAF)
26. The GAU-8 30mm cannon is the most powerful gun ever fitted in an aircraft. Mounted to the left of the A-10's centreline, it can fire 120 rounds in the first two seconds. (Fairchild Republic)

26▶

27–31. During a test at the Indian Springs Bomb Range, Nevada, four Rockeyes show why they are such effective ground attack weapons. After release (photograph 27) the canisters break apart to dispense their submunitions (28, 29). The bomblets impact as the empty canister halves flutter to the ground (30, 31). (USAF)

27, 28, 29 ▶

▼30

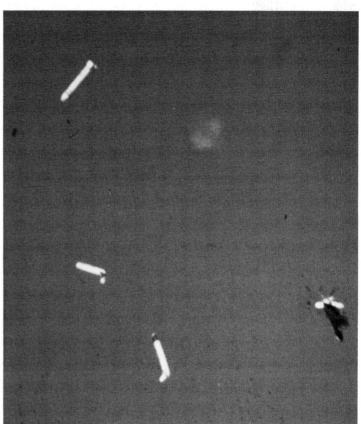

31▼

51

▲32 ▼33

34 ▲

◀35

32. A 23rd TFW A-10 pulls up as its practice bombs hit the bullseye during 'Gunsmoke 81' tactical competitions. (USAF)

33. An A-10 swathed in its own gun gases during a firing pass. (USAF)

34. Armament technicians move an early version of 'the Dragon' into position. The special ground equipment is used to load the linkless 30mm ammunition into the GAU-8's drum. (USAF)

35. Here, 30mm rounds are placed on to 'the Dragon's chain drive and carried directly into the ammunition drum. The A-10 carries a maximum of 1,350 rounds. (USAF)

36. One of the newest improvements to the A-10 is this gun gas deflector, which directs smoke below the aircraft, keeping the windscreen clear and the turbine blades free of gas. (Author)

37. The inertia of depleted uranium, which has a greater mass than lead, is focused at a spike in the nose of the armour-piercing round. The resulting force will pass through the upper armour of any tank in service. (USAF)

38. High over the California desert, the first prototype flies an icing test. A solution sprayed from a KC-135 tanker turns yellow as it changes to ice on the fighter's wing, tail and engine. (USAF)

39. Live 500lb bombs wait to be loaded on to the last pre-production aircraft at Edwards AFB, California. This A-10's unusual mottled camouflage was applied with thin coats of white over a black base primer. (USAF)

▲36 ▼37

▲ 40

40. The same aircraft was involved in cold weather tests in Alaska in 1977. The pilot on this mission, Major Rusty Guideon, would eject from this very aircraft in 1978 when both engines failed during gun gas tests – see photograph 106. (USAF)

41. The instrument panel of the A-10, uncluttered and easy to read. (USAF)

42. A 355th TFW aircraft takes off during the A-10's first deployment to Germany in 1977. (USAF)

43. Two 354th TFW A-10s show their 'Charcoal Lizard' camouflage over the Carolinas. (USAF)

▼ 41

42 ▲   43 ▲

▲44

44. The first 'Lizard' scheme was tested in the summer of 1980. This 57th TTW aircraft, from Nellis AFB, Nevada, used a lighter grey than was later approved for production camouflage. (Wally van Winkle)

45. A clean view of the second production camouflage scheme on a 355th TFW aircraft, 1978. (Dave Menard)

▼45

46. A Pave Penny AAS-35 laser seeker hangs from its pylon beside the cockpit of this 57th Fighter Weapons Wing 'Hog', early 1978. The aircraft was in Germany to test the new Imaging Infra-Red (IIR) Maverick, the AGM-65D, which can be seen beneath the left wing. (USAF)

46▶

▲47

47. A training version of the television-guided AGM-65B Maverick, seen in 1983. Training Mavericks have neither guidance fins nor rocket motors. (Wally van Winkle)

48. Standard electronic countermeasures for the A-10 consist of one ALQ-119 on an outboard pylon. The pod is mounted forward on the rack, to leave room for the speed brakes to open. (Wally van Winkle)

49. Supports are checked on a 700-gallon external fuel tank. The

ferry tank is the same model as that carried by the F-111. (USAF)

50. (Next spread) A new 'Warthog' rolls down the line at Fairchild Republic's Hagerstown production facility. Two machines in the background wear yellow primer coats, but this aircraft carries the early asymmetrical camouflage: the dark right wing and engine pod are opposed on the left by the light wing and pod. The pattern is reversed on the undersides. (Fairchild Republic)

▼48   49▶

▲51　▼52

51. The asymmetrical scheme seen on most Davis-Monthan A-10s during 1976 was relieved only by a small black 355th TFW shield over the fuselage insignia and a TAC shield and 'DM' code on the fin. (Fairchild Republic)
52. Fresh from the factory, an A-10 touches down at Davis-Monthan. Within months, the asymmetrical grey camouflage would begin to oxidize and 'chalk up' under the desert sun. (Fairchild Republic)
53. In early 1977 the A-10 production camouflage was changed to a graded scheme using a dark grey above and a lighter grey below. Test flown over Maryland, this early example of the second production scheme still carries the code '134' on the fin in black water-soluble paint, indicating this as the 134th A-10A off the line. (Fairchild Republic)
54. Another A-10 in the second production scheme lands during tests at Bicycle Dry Lake, California, June 1977. Note the split ailerons, which act as speed brakes. (Fairchild Republic)

55. A then-unique feature of the second production camouflage was a false canopy painted below the fuselage. This part of the deceptive paint scheme was invented and patented by the aviation artist Keith Ferris. (Fairchild Republic)

56. The year 1977 saw many international visits by A-10s from Davis-Monthan and Nellis Air Force Bases. Taking off for firepower demonstrations in Korea, this aircraft mounts eight Rockeyes and two live Mavericks. (USAF)

55 ▶

▼56

57 ▲

◄58

57. Two 354th TFW
A-10s fly over the local
resort area near the base
at Myrtle Beach, South
Carolina. (USAF)
58. Against the sky, the
second production
scheme made the A-10
difficult to see. Special
paints also helped to
reduce the effectiveness
of infra-red and radar
tracking. (USAF)

59. Seen against the ground, the light grey camouflage proved to be problematic. 'Aggressor' pilots during Operation 'JAWS' (Joint Attack Weapons System) could often find A-10s visually before locating them on radar. (USAF)

60. During 'JAWS II' in November 1977, two aircraft wore spotted schemes consisting of several tones of earth. The camouflage was slightly more visible against the sky, but far more effective seen against the ground. (Fairchild Republic)

61. Rolling through the hills at Fort Ligget-Hunter, California, a 'Warthog' demonstrates its manoeuvrability to an Air Force range officer. For such exercises, external pods under the aircraft relayed data on flight profiles via ground-based antennas (visible). Note the open slats on the wing leading edge, which prevent the air flow from stalling the engines. (USAF)

◀59

60 ▲   61▼

▲62 ▼63

▼64

62–64. Another A-10 makes its run toward the press during 'JAWS II'. (*Monterey Peninsula Herald*)

65. The agile A-10 requires a commensurate mental agility in its pilot: this turn is performed within sixty feet of the ground. The hills mask the sound of the 'Hog's approach; from other locations, scouts radio enemy positions. (USAF)

66. Target identified, the 'Warthog' pops over the hill to begin its firing run. A-10s generally fight in pairs, teamed with Army attack and scout helicopters, ground observers and field artillery. (Fairchild Republic)

65▲   66▼

▲68   ▼69

67. (Previous spread) 'Warthogs' go through final assembly at Fairchild's Hagerstown plant. Note the fuselage stores rack in the left foreground. (Fairchild Republic)
68. Tactics are a key to the A-10's survivability. In this photograph a 355th TFW pilot uses ground smoke as a screen during desert manoeuvres in 1977. (USAF)
69. Nature's warthog is named for the wart-like bumps on its face;

the flying version of the warthog has its bumps on the other end, since there are few flush fuselage rivets aft of the wing. (USAF)
70. Two 81st TFW A-10s bank over the English countryside, 1983. (USAF)
71. One of the four 57th TTW A-10s used to test the spotted camouflage scheme stands in the desert sun at Nellis AFB, Nevada, in early 1978. (Mick Roth)

▲72   ▼73

72, 73. A 'Warthog' with an extra sting: this 57th TTW A-10 carries two Sidewinder air-to-air missiles, which greatly enhance defensive capabilities. (USAF)
74. An A-10 of the 81st TFW, RAF Bentwater, England, in 1983. (USAF)
75. The first pre-production A-10 approaches a desert bombing range during the operational test programme. (USAF)

▲76 ▼77

76. A 355th TFW A-10 tucks in its landing gear during an orientation flight in Germany, 1977. (USAF)

77. The first pre-production airframe was modified into the two-seat YA-10B for night and adverse weather operations. Though much was learned about electronics modifications to the 'Warthog', no additional two-seaters were produced. (USAF)

78. When the US Air Force asked for proposals for a new ground camouflage scheme in 1978, a grey or one of two greens was suggested: in the event, all three colours were applied. This early production A-10, which had also tested one of the spotted 'JAWS' schemes, wears the second variation of the three-colour camouflage. (USAF)

79. In February 1977 two 355th TFW A-10s were used for a 'surge test' at Gila Bend, Arizona. In eleven hours, the two machines flew thirty-four sorties, dropped 70,000lb of bombs and fired 3,610 rounds of 30mm ammunition. Simulating combat conditions, reloading and refuelling was accomplished with engines still running. Here the pilot waits in his cockpit during one such 'pit stop'. (USAF)

79▼

▲80   ▼81

80. The wisdom behind the A-10's design peculiarities helped make the surge test a success: ground crews reload and refuel without special stands or ladders, while the running engines are high enough to present no dangers. In the background, one pilot leaves the cockpit as his replacement prepares to board for the next sortie. (USAF)

81. Another 500lb bomb is moved into position during the surge test. (USAF)

82. A civilian on the A-10 test team checks landing gear for fluid leaks. The main forgings for the left and right gear struts are identical, reducing production costs and spares requirements. (Goodyear)

83. At ceremonies for the roll-out of the hundredth A-10A, company officials announced the selection of 'Thunderbolt II' as the A-10's official nickname. Red decals on the nose were included for the unveiling. (Fairchild Republic)

82 ▲   83 ▼

▲84   ▼85

84. Two 355th TFW
A-10s were leased to
Fairchild Republic for
display at the 1977 Paris
Air Show. The second
aircraft, bearing the air
show number '97' on the
engine pod, crashed
during a demo flight.
Three 700-gallon ferry
tanks were mounted for
the transatlantic trip.
(USAF)
85. Camouflage netting
helps to hide one of the
four 333rd TFTS A-10s
participating in exercises
on the lake bed at
Bicycle Dry Lake,
California, in June 1976.
(Fairchild Republic)
86. The Bicycle Dry
Lake operations were
terminated by flash
floods. Before moving
out, the aircraft and
crews had operated
through extreme
temperatures, strong
winds and dust storms
like the one in this
photograph. (Fairchild
Republic)

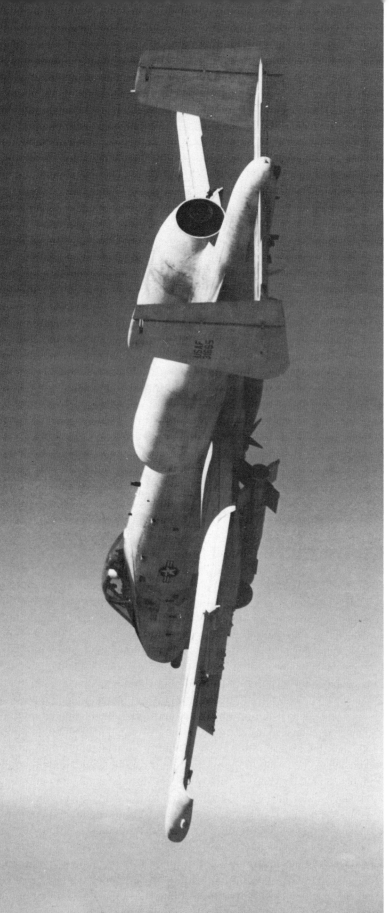

87. Diving from altitude, a pre-production A-10 prepares to deliver a pair of 2,000lb guided bombs; most A-10 attacks are made from far lower levels. (USAF)

88. A trio of 355th TFW A-10s stand ready in open revetments during a 1978 deployment to Europe. (Fairchild Republic)

89. 'Warthogs' were first assigned to the 81st TFW at RAF Bentwaters and RAF Woodbridge, England, in late 1978. This example sits inside an open 'TAB V' shelter following a light snowstorm. (Fairchild Republic)

◀ 87

▲90 ▼91

90. A pair of 81st TFW
'Warthogs' roll away from the
camera during a training flight
over England, 1982. Electronics
pods and missiles have
traditionally been painted white
to protect their internal circuits
from heat, but newer systems
are being camouflaged for lower
visibility. (USAF)
91. A 57th FWW A-10 refuels
from the prototype KC-10
tanker aircraft, 1982. The new
tanker was tested against most
types on USAF and Navy
inventories to establish
optimum mission profiles.
(McDonnell Douglas)
92. A 30mm ammunition loader
is moved to a 354th TFW
'Warthog' during a quick turn-
round at Myrtle Beach AFB,
1980. (USAF)
93. Teamwork during
Operation 'Team Spirit 85' in
Korea: the wing commander's
F-16 from the 8th TFW ('The
Wolfpack') flies off the wing of
a 25th TFS A-10. Both aircraft
are based in Korea. (USAF)

92▲   93▼

▲94

94. Speed brakes open for rapid descent, an A-10 drops past a bridge to land on a German autobahn during operations in early 1984. (USAF)

95. A pair of A-10s from the Connecticut Air National Guard's 103rd TFG take off at Bradley Field, Connecticut. (Don Linn)

96. A two-plane section from the 18th TFS, seen from a tanker high over Alaska. The 18th is the Alaskan Air Command's only A-10 squadron. (USAF)

▼95

96▶

▲97   ▼98

99▲

97. In June 1980 the 917th TFG (Barksdale AFB, Louisiana) became the first Air Force Reserve unit to fly the A-10. The fin tops were painted red when this 1982 photo was taken. (Tom Chee via Don Linn)
98. In April 1979 Connecticut and Massachusetts boasted the first Air National Guard units to receive new aircraft direct from the production line. This is one of the A-10s flown by the 104th TFG, Massachusetts ANG. The tail band is red with white stars and a black centreline. (Don Linn)
99. Two early production 'Warthogs' fly a operational test with the 355th TFW at Davis-Monthan AFB, Arizona. The Wing's 'DM' tail codes had not been applied when this photograph was taken. (Fairchild Republic)
100. The first two pre-production aircraft flank a later machine wearing the asymmetrical camouflage scheme. Note the unusual nacelle location of the national insignia on the nearest A-10. (Fairchild Republic)

100▼

▲101 ▼102

103▶

101. Flaps full down at 20 degrees, a 354th TFW 'Warthog' poses for the public at a Canadian Air Show in 1978. (G. L. Marshall)

102. During 1982 exercises in Alaska a single 18th TFS A-10 was partially camouflaged with removable white paint. In contrast, the green areas of the airframe appear almost black. (USAF)

103. A crew chief removes his communications plug before his A-10 clears the ramp. (USAF)

104. An A-10 brakes at the hardstanding following an operational test flight. Multiple ejector racks under the fuselage have been made safe, as shown by the red remove-before-flight tags. (Fairchild Republic)

▲105

105. The 174th TFG, New York Air National Guard, has been flying the A-10 since June 1979. The unit's *nom de guerre*, 'The Boys from Syracuse', is visible on the engine nacelle. (Don Linn)

106. Major Rusty Guideon ejected from the final pre-production A-10 when gun gas tests caused flame-outs in both engines. The rapid approach of the desert floor allowed no time for the engines to be restarted. See also photographs 39 and 40. (USAF)

107. The A-10's two nacelles are fitted with General Electric's TF-34-100 engine. A turbofan, 85 per cent of its thrust is cold air generated by the fan. (Rob Stern)

108. Engine changes do not require heavy cranes: a portable winch is mounted atop the nacelle, allowing two men to lower the engine to a dolly. (Rob Stern)

▼106

107▲   108▼

109. An aircraft can be camouflaged and a missile can be camouflaged, but a plume of smoke cannot be disguised. Here a Maverick leaves the launch rail of a pre-production airframe, 1976. (USAF)

110. A Maverick is carried to a waiting A-10 during Operation 'Bright Star 81' in Egypt. (USAF)

111. A 'Warthog' makes its approach, landing in Egypt after a 'Bright Star' sortie. (USAF)

112. A-10A No. 1 was the first 'Warthog' to feature single-point refuelling from the left wheel sponson. This 'kneecap' position can be easily reached from the ground, speeding refuelling during quick turn-rounds. (USAF)

109▶

▼110

▲113 ▼114

113. The second A-10 prototype was 'doctored' to look like a production airframe and shipped around the US for static displays. The aircraft has since been turned over to the Air Force Museum at Wright-Patterson AFB, Ohio. (Author)

114. The ground crew 'owns' an aircraft every bit as much as the pilot. Working as a team, this crew chief and assistant test the systems of their charge. (USAF)

115. An Air Force test pilot prepares for take-off in one of the pre-production airframes. His ejection seat is the Escapac used on the first A-10s. The explosive wires overhead would shatter the transparency to facilitate an ejection. (USAF)

116. Air compressing over the wings condenses moisture during a high-*g* pull-out over South Carolina. This aircraft is assigned to the 354th TFW. (USAF)

115▲ 116▼

▲117　▼118

117. A 355th TFW A-10 is readied for take-off in Germany during Operation 'Coronet Bantam', the first deployment of the 'Warthog' to Europe, 1977. (USAF)
118. After the mission, the pilot discusses the plane's performance with his ground crew. (USAF)